Reading for informat

C000270404

Contents

Teachers' notes

The aims of this book

• To introduce beginning readers to the different forms of non-fiction texts.
• To provide activities which encourage readers to read and reflect upon non-fiction texts.
• To help children to respond actively to non-fiction by writing the information in different forms.
• To model ways of reading and writing non-fiction texts which could be applied to other texts.
• To familiarise children with the different forms of presenting non-fiction, such as maps, charts and diagrams.
• To extend children's understanding of extracting information from non-fiction texts.

Introduction

This book of photocopiable pages aims to help children gain understanding and information from simple texts. They are intended as 'models' of the kinds of texts that readers of non-fiction need to be able to interpret. It is hoped that teachers will use them to develop their own ideas, linking the subject matter more closely to the topics that the children are studying in their classrooms. The sheets include various activities grouped under more general headings,

identifying the main skill involved (see Contents above). All these skills are needed if children are to read information texts with understanding. Introducing these skills very early into children's reading will prepare them for the demands that they will meet from longer texts and enable them to access information. This will encourage them to undertake further research more confidently with interest and enjoyment.

The difficulties of non-fiction texts

Reading non-fiction requires a special style of reading. Most information books do not have a story-line, so there is no natural sequence to help the reader remember what has gone before or to predict what may happen next.

Children have hundreds of stories read to them at the early stages of reading and they become very familiar with the patterns of stories. They learn how to use illustrations to help with the interpretation of the text and how to predict events from the context. When they first meet non-fiction, they need a different set of reading skills if they are to succeed at reading for information.

In non-fiction books the illustrations are not merely decorative, they are a vehicle for conveying the meaning of a topic. The information presented in a graph, chart or diagram needs to be studied carefully and interpreted if the rest of the text is to be comprehensible. Understanding information presented graphically is an essential part of reading non-fiction and children need to be aware of this. Unless they are shown how to use these forms they can easily become confused; all too often they apply their fiction reading skills to the reading of non-fiction.

Notes on individual activities

Pages 5 to 6: Following instructions

These activities are designed to reflect the likely experiences of young children and to show them the need to read a text with care and extract the necessary information. They are then required to transfer this knowledge to the outline pictures.

Extension activity

• Ask the children to suggest an activity that they do, for example playing football, dancing, going on holiday. Ask them to decide what articles are needed for each particular activity, and in what quantity. What drawing would they suggest for the outline picture to best illustrate this activity? Talk to them about the need for labelling such diagrams so that other children can understand the information. Show them, by drawing on a board, how this is displayed.

Pages 7 to 8: Making a list

These activities give children practice in writing items in list form. This is a very important skill which is frequently used in everyday life. The children should look at the picture and labels and then list the relevant items.

Page 9: The alien planet

This early level of map work will help establish a firm foundation for the important skills and concepts necessary for map interpretation. Children need to be able to follow simple directions orally before they try to plot this kind of experience on to paper. This activity is a check sheet to establish how much of this type of positional language the child can use.

Extension activities

• Play simple activity games in which the children can practise positional language, for example 'Sit on your chair', 'Sit under your chair', 'Sit beside your chair', 'Sit behind your chair', 'Sit in front of your chair.'
• Make sentence cards with simple instructions written on them. Let the children read the card and then follow the instruction; for example, 'Put your pencil under your book', 'Put your book near your friend', 'Put your crayon on top of your

paper', 'Put your paper inside your book', 'Put your pencil above your table', 'Put your pencil below your table.'
• Choose different children to be the instructor and let them give simple directions to the group, either orally or by showing and reading your instruction cards.

Pages 10 to 11: The swimming pool/At the fun park

These are simple activities in which the children are expected to translate their visual knowledge into diagrams.

Before using these sheets, it is essential that the teacher has demonstrated to the group how and why maps are devised. Begin by showing the class how they could make a 'map' of the classroom. Ask them how they would represent the various pieces of furniture on the plan. Show them how other published material has represented the same articles, for instance tables as circles or rectangles. When the plan has been completed on the board, let the children identify an object on the plan and then find it in the classroom.

This work could then be extended to the playground and to the school environment. Remember that even some very able children need considerable practice in interpreting maps and plans before they become really familiar with this way of representing knowledge.

Pages 12 to 13: Alphabetical order

It is essential that children both know and constantly use alphabetical order. These pages can be used as a check to see to what extent children have mastered simple alphabetical order. They often seem to have acquired this skill early in their school life but then 'forget' it! This is probably due to a lack of frequent practice. Do take every opportunity to explain how and why they need to know the order of the alphabet and do give them time to use it for themselves. It is all too easy to find the 'word' or encyclopedia entry for the child who seems to be taking too long, but this is to deny those who need it most the chance to become really familiar with this essential skill.

Pages 14 to 17: Information from signs

These sheets are aimed at helping children to recognise the importance of extracting information from environmental print. Children who come to school often have no difficulty recognising 'The World of Toys' or 'Burger Bar'. This knowledge may need to be refined so that they appreciate the significance of environmental print instead of just seeing it as background wallpaper.

Extension activities

• Write simple information on the notice-board and draw the children's attention to it.
• Write short letters to the individual children in the class and leave the envelope with the child's name and address on it pinned to the notice-board. Children love getting letters, especially from the teacher!
• Encourage the children to be responsible for some of the classroom signs.
• Write simple instructions and place them for all the children to read, for example, 'This door leads to the cloakroom.'
• Go round the school with the children and make a list of all the signs that they can find.
• Ask the children to collect a similar list on their way home. Talk about the importance of reading the signs.

Pages 18 to 21: Note-taking

It is unlikely that the children are familiar with this skill and considerable preparation is needed before these sheets should be given to them. When introducing them to reading non-fiction, the teacher needs to demonstrate how such texts are read: the reading is slow; the reader stops and reflects upon the information; then the reader records the information in some way, so that it can be used on future occasions. A useful way to demonstrate this is to use a highlighter pen and mark the vital information for the children on the page. Let them discuss which words are of importance. Show the group the importance of headings and subheadings. Finally, show them how this information can be tabulated into charts.

Extension activities

• Encourage the children to think of other subjects, for example pets. Write up the knowledge that they have about these subjects, then ask the children what else they need to find out. Show them how to find this information from other sources. Encourage them to devise a chart on which to present it. When they are familiar with this, change the activity round and ask the children to work in pairs from the chart and to 'rewrite' it as a short piece of continuous text.

Pages 22 to 25: Classifying

This important method of extracting information will need careful introduction. It has relevance throughout the curriculum, especially with science and mathematics. Very young children need to start looking for common characteristics within materials, and sorting according to their own criteria, as well as by suggested criteria. They are likely to enter school with very different levels of understanding of how to classify information and it is essential for teachers to establish the extent of each child's understanding before expecting them to be able to undertake classifying activities.

In order to support the child, some pictures are provided around the border so that she or he can begin to tabulate from these rather than from an empty page.

Extension activities

• Many children will need to sort objects into various groups as a tactile activity before they are ready to do this on paper. It may be sensible to start with grouping according to certain colours, then moving on to such things as animals versus plants, and finally deciding how to group within the animal group, for instance grass eaters versus meat eaters.
• Let the children provide headings for their own charts and make these into tasks for their friends to do, for example hot and cold. The border could contain illustrations taken from magazines or catalogues.

Pages 26 to 29: Labelling

These activities are linked to the History National Curriculum at Key Stage 1. The topics chosen are likely to be introduced at this stage. Discussion of the past will be necessary with children in the early years as this is a very difficult concept for them.

In order to show them the place and importance of labelling from text the teacher needs to demonstrate how to do this. Using a highlighter pen to emphasise the important information can be useful. The first activity is linked to the child's own lifestyle and this is then taken further on the following sheets. Labelling diagrams from text is an important skill and is probably the first step towards helping children become the eventual creators of diagrams.

Extension activities

• Children draw and label their own picture.
• Children work in pairs and label each other's pictures.
• Children listen to a recording of a simple description of either a person or a place and then represent this as a labelled drawing.

Pages 30 to 32: Writing instructions

These pictures are designed to help children organise information and write simple instructions. The teacher needs to introduce such work orally before the children embark upon trying to write 'restricted' texts. When they have understood the need for clarity and simplicity, the teacher can show them how to achieve this by the way in which the information can be presented.

Remember that children are usually being encouraged to write at greater length when they write stories. Writing instructions requires succinct language and they find writing briefly is very difficult!

Extension activities

• Select a subject such as instructions on how the children may sit for lunch in the school. Ask the children to tell you all the things that a new child would need to know and write these down on the board. Let the children edit these instructions with you, deciding on the order. Finally, write the instructions on large sheets of paper and display in the classroom. Refer to this model when showing children how to write instructions.

National Curriculum: English

The activities in this book support the following requirements of the PoS for KS1 for the National Curriculum for English:

Reading
● Pupils should be introduced to and should read information, both in print and on screen. They should be encouraged to make use of a range of sources of information;
● The materials read and discussed should be used to stimulate pupils' imagination and enthusiasm. They should include:
 • the use of a variety of organisational and presentational techniques;
● Pupils should be taught the alphabet;
● Pupils should be taught to use reference materials for different purposes. They should be taught about the structural devices for organising information.

Writing
● Pupils should be helped to understand the value of writing as a means of remembering, communicating, organising and developing ideas and information;
● Pupils should be given opportunities to write in response to a variety of stimuli;
● Pupils should be taught to organise and present their writing in different ways... They should be taught to write in a range of forms, incorporating some of the different characteristics of those forms. The range should include a variety of narratives, ... notes, *eg lists...*; and messages, *eg ... instructions*.

Scottish 5–14 Curriculum: English language

Attainment outcome	Strand	Attainment target	Level
Reading	Reading for information	Find an item of information from an informational text.	A
Writing	Functional writing	Write briefly for a simple practical purpose.	A
Listening	Listening for information, instructions and directions	Listen and show that they understand and can use what has been heard.	A

Scottish 5–14 Curriculum: Environmental studies

Attainment outcome	Strand
Place, time and society	Understanding maps
Investigating	Finding out from specified sources

See inside back cover for Northern Ireland Curriculum links

The fruit bowl

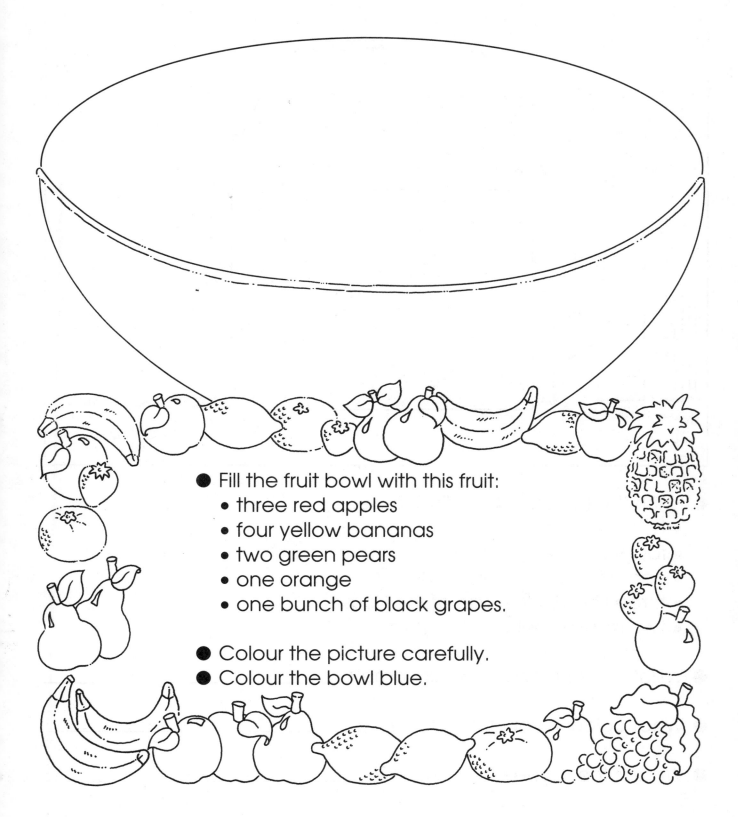

● Fill the fruit bowl with this fruit:
  • three red apples
  • four yellow bananas
  • two green pears
  • one orange
  • one bunch of black grapes.

● Colour the picture carefully.
● Colour the bowl blue.

The house

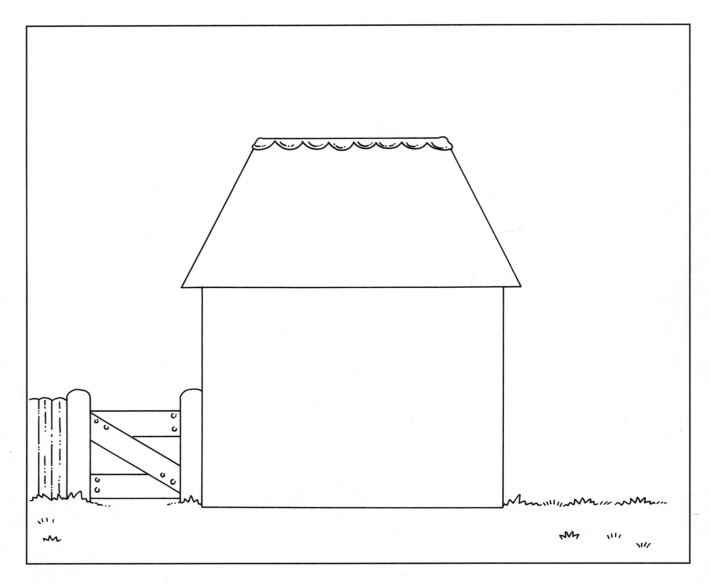

● Finish the picture by adding these:
  - two chimneys
  - four windows
  - one door with number 10 on it
  - three trees at the side of the house
  - two people behind the gate.

● What is the number of your home? _____

● What colour is your front door? _____

● What is the name of your road? _____

Laying the table

● Look at the picture below. List all the things that were used to lay this table.

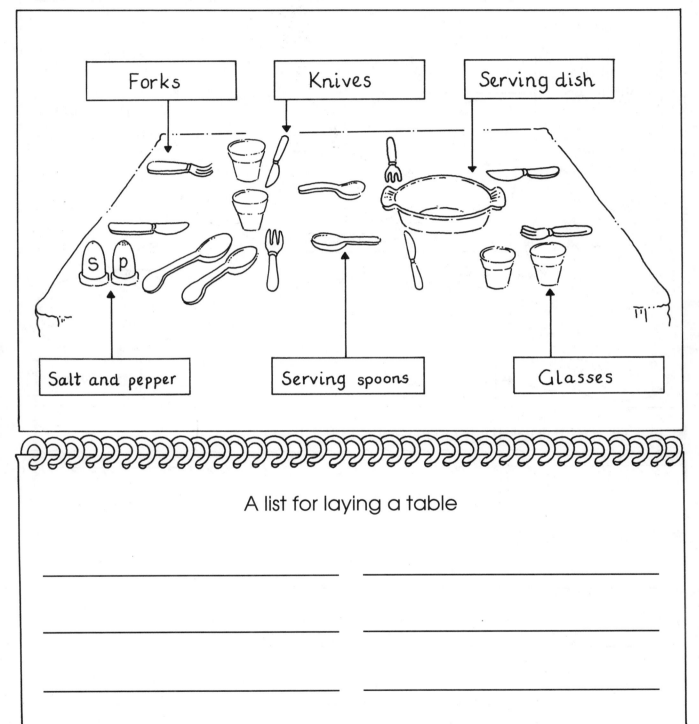

A list for laying a table

_____   _____

_____   _____

_____   _____

● Think of two more things to put on the table.

_____   _____

Having a party

Emma is six years old. She is having a party with four of her friends.

● List all the things that are needed for the party.

_____   _____

_____   _____

_____   _____

_____   _____

● Think of two more things to eat at the party.

_____   _____

● Name _____

The alien planet

● Describe this picture. The words below will help you.

near	**inside**	**in front of**
beside	**down**	**across** **behind**

The rocket has landed _____ a volcano. A spaceman

walks _____ the steps to get to the space buggy.

Some aliens are watching from _____ the rocks.

They live _____ the craters. The spaceman is going to

walk _____ the ground to put a flag _____

some large rocks _____ the aliens.

● **Name** _____

The swimming pool

● Look at this picture and answer the questions below.

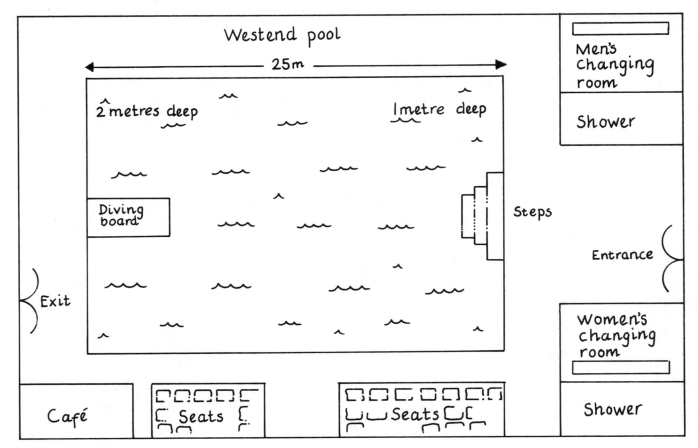

- How long is the pool?

_____

- What is the name of the pool?

_____

- What is on the same side as the entrance?

_____

- What is at the opposite end of the pool to the steps?

_____

- What is next to the café?

_____

● Name _____

At the fun park

● Look at this picture.

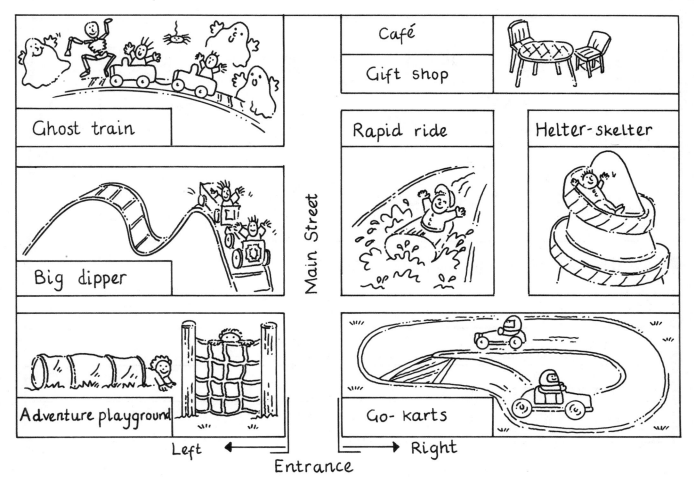

● Answer these questions.

- Is the café on the left or the right of the main street?

_____

- What is inside the entrance on the left-hand side?

_____

- If you turn right past the go-karts, what is on your left?

_____

- You want a ride on the ghost train. How would you get there?

_____

● **Name** _____

Animal names

● Here are the names of some animals.

elephant   rabbit   kangaroo   jaguar

wolf   x-ray fish

mouse   tortoise   goat   quail

hedgehog

squirrel   anteater   penguin

● Put the names in alphabetical order.

a _____   n _____

b _____   o _____

c _____   p _____

d _____   q _____

e _____   r _____

f _____   s _____

g _____   t _____

h _____   u _____

i _____   v _____

j _____   w _____

k _____   x _____

l _____   y _____

m _____   z _____

● Think of some more animals to complete your chart.
You can use a dictionary to help you.

Girls' and boys' names

● Here are the names of some children.

Winston   Ian   Quentin   Duncan

Zoe

Guy

Andrew   Vicky   Harpreet   Ursula

Nadine   Yasmin   Oliver   Hamid

● Put the names in alphabetical order.

a _____ n _____

b _____ o _____

c _____ p _____

d _____ q _____

e _____ r _____

f _____ s _____

g _____ t _____

h _____ u _____

i _____ v _____

j _____ w _____

k _____ x _____

l _____ y _____

m _____ z _____

● Think of some more names to complete your chart.
Don't forget – names begin with capital letters.

At the garage

● Look at the picture carefully.

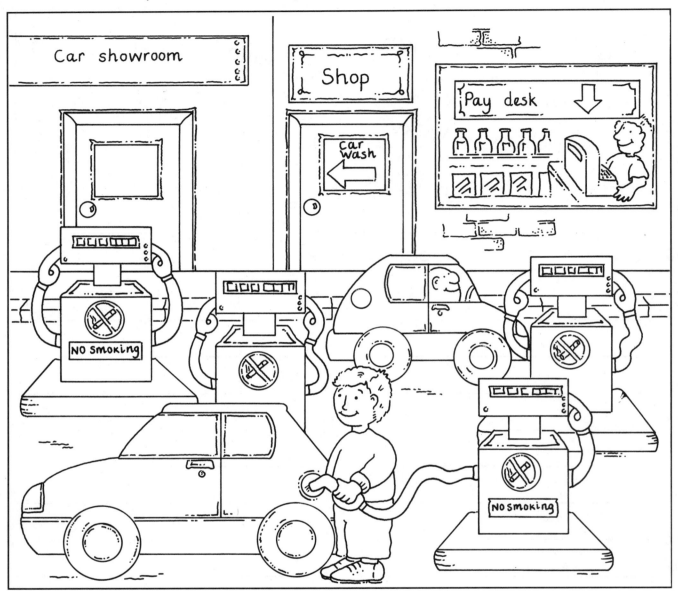

● Answer these questions.

- How many cars are being filled with petrol? _____

- Where do you pay? _____

- Where do you go to clean the car?_____

- Could you buy a car here?_____

- Why is there a 'No smoking' sign? _____

_____

At the station

● Look at the picture carefully.

● Answer these questions.

- Where do you think the train is going? _____

- Where could you wait if you arrived early? _____

- What is the name of the town? _____

- What time does the clock say? _____

- If you were hungry what could you find to eat? _____

● Name _____

At the supermarket

● Look at the picture carefully.

● Answer these questions.

• Which checkout has the most people waiting? _____

• What is reduced in price? _____

• Where are the trolleys parked? _____

• What does the sign saying 'Baskets only' mean?

_____

• Why are the sweets near the checkout?

_____

At the airport

● Look at the picture carefully.

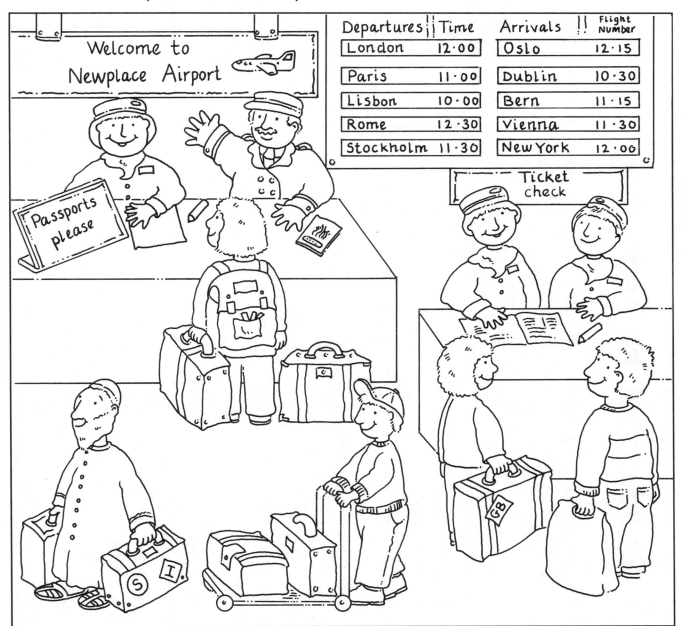

Departures	Time	Arrivals	Flight Number
London	12·00	Oslo	12·15
Paris	11·00	Dublin	10·30
Lisbon	10·00	Bern	11·15
Rome	12·30	Vienna	11·30
Stockholm	11·30	New York	12·00

Welcome to Newplace Airport

Passports please

Ticket check

● Answer these questions.

• What is the name of the airport?_____

• Where are the aeroplanes going? _____

_____

• Why do you need to check your ticket?_____

• What other desk do you need to go to? _____

Read about the hedgehog

• Make some notes on the chart. Use the headings to help you.

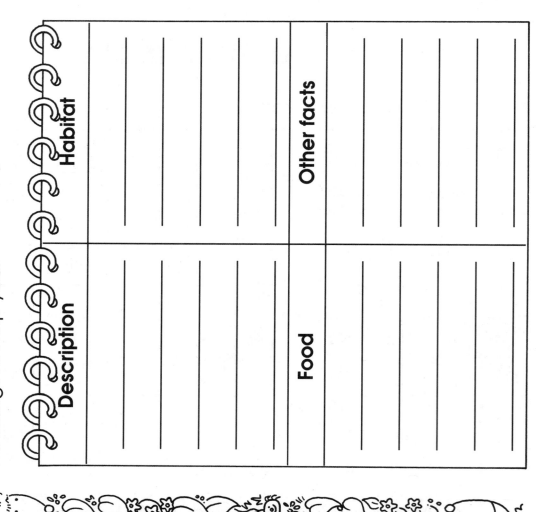

Description	Habitat

Food	Other facts

Hedgehogs are small mammals. They have hard brown spines on their backs. If a hedgehog is frightened it rolls up into a ball. Their legs are short with five sharp claws on each foot.

Hedgehogs have long noses and a good sense of smell, but their eyesight is not very good. When they are hungry they eat slugs, spiders, snails, beetles and worms.

In the winter hedgehogs hibernate. They make nests from leaves. They find sheltered places, in ditches or under hedges, where they sleep in the cold weather.

Read about the snail

● Make some notes on the chart. Use the headings to help you.

Description	Habitat

Food	Other facts

Snails can be found in the garden. They have a hard shell which is a part of their bodies.

When snails are hungry they look for food with their horns. On top of each horn is a little eye.

They eat leaves. They like cabbages and lettuces. Snails often go to sleep inside their shells during the day. They find a sheltered place to sleep. At night they come out to look for food. They leave a slimy trail behind them as they move. This helps them to slide over stones and dry ground.

In the winter snails hibernate. They make a wall of hard slime and go to sleep in their shells.

Read about the frog

● Make some notes on the chart. Use the headings to help you.

Description	Habitat

Food	Other facts

Frogs live in or near the water. They need damp places because they breathe through their smooth and shiny skin. They use their long back legs and webbed feet to swim, leap and jump.

Frogs have long sticky tongues to catch insects and slugs. Frogs' eggs are called frogspawn. Tadpoles hatch from the eggs and grow into frogs.

Read about the sparrow

● Make some notes on the chart. Use the headings to help you.

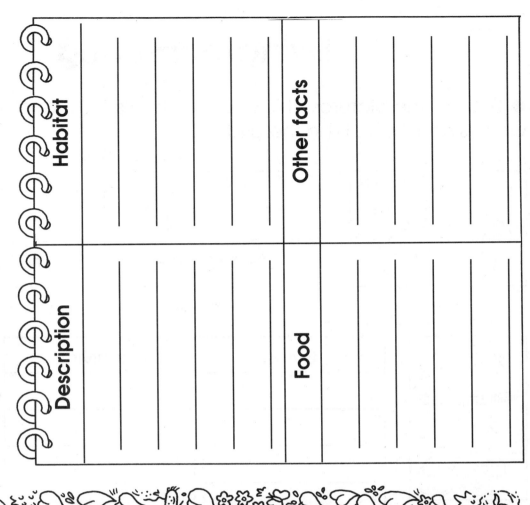

Description	Habitat

Food	Other facts

Sparrows are small garden birds. The female sparrow is brown and grey. The male sparrow has a dark grey patch on top of his head and a black breast.

Sparrows make their nests in hedges and keep them well hidden. The nest is made from straw, grass and small feathers. It is not very tidy.

The female sparrow lays her eggs in the nest and looks after them. The eggs are pale grey with brown spots all over. She spends her time sitting on the eggs until they hatch. Then both the male and the female sparrow feed insects to the fledglings until they learn to fly.

Living/non-living

● Look at the pictures. Think about what is living and what is non-living. Fill in the grid.

Living	Non-living

chair

baby

car

lamp

plant

cat

snake

jumper

fish

television

● Think of some other things to complete your chart.

Town/country

● Look at the pictures. Think about what might be found in the town or in the country. Fill in the grid.

cottage

supermarket

cows

factory

block of flats

Town	Country

traffic lights

tractor

fields

horses

● Think of some more things to complete your chart.

Old/new

● Look at the pictures. Think about what might be old and what might be new. Fill in the grid.

car

castle

mountain bike

trainers

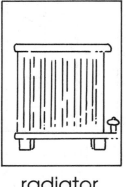

radiator

Old	New

computer

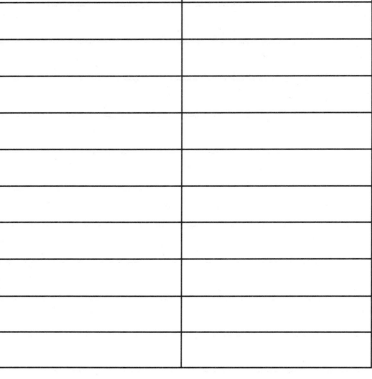

aeroplane

steam train

thatched cottage

candle

● Find some more things to add to your chart.

● Name _____

Natural/man-made materials

● Look at the pictures. Think about which are made from natural materials and which from man-made materials. Fill in the grid.

sand

tyre

stones

mug

tree

Natural	Man-made

waterfall

book

lunch box

coal

window

● Find some more things to add to your chart.

Clothes today

● Look at this drawing of a girl. Label the drawing using the words below.

jeans	sweatshirt	anorak
scarf	gloves	trainers	baseball cap

● What clothes do you like to wear when you go out to play?

An Edwardian girl

● Read the description and then label this drawing of the Edwardian girl.

This is an Edwardian girl dressed in her best clothes.
She is wearing a velvet frock with a lace collar, with a lace petticoat underneath. The cap she is wearing is called a bob cap. On her feet she has high button shoes.

● Can you find out what an Edwardian boy would wear?

A Viking girl

A long time ago Viking girls looked like this.

● Label the picture. The writing below tells you all about her.

A Viking girl wore a linen shift with a woollen dress over
the top of it. She wore woollen stockings and leather shoes.
When it was cold she wore a cloak with a hood as well.
She fastened this with a bronze brooch. She also wore a
silver ring on her finger.

● What else can you find out about Viking clothes?

A Roman soldier

A very long time ago Roman soldiers dressed like this.

● Label the picture. The writing below tells you all about him.

A Roman soldier wore a tunic and short leather trousers with a wide leather belt. On his feet he wore leather sandals. A Roman soldier always carried a dagger and a shield. His head was protected by a bronze helmet.

● What else can you find out about Roman soldiers?

Looking after a pet

● Write the instructions for each picture.

How to have a healthy pet

_____

_____

_____

_____

_____

_____

_____

_____

_____

_____

_____

_____

● Using the back of this page, make a list of other pets.

How to plant seeds

● Write the instructions for each picture.

● Using the back of this page, make a list of flowers you know.

How to keep healthy

● Write the instructions for each picture.

Your health

● Using the back of this page, make a list of foods that are good for you.